MOM AND ME

PICTURES AND WORDS BY

MIELA FORD

SCHOLASTIC INC.
New York Toronto London Auckland Sydney
Mexico City New Delhi Hong Kong

ISBN 0-439-09777-0

12 11 10 9 8 7 6 5 4 3 2 1   9/9 0 1 2 3 4/0

Printed in the U.S.A.   08

First Scholastic printing, November 1999

The full-color photographs were reproduced from 35-mm slides.
The text type is ITC Kabel Medium.

FOR MAX

I'm awake.

My mom's asleep.

Should I wake her up?

Come on, Mom!

Get up with me.

Let's go.

I want to play.

Roly-poly,

poly-roly.

In . . .

and out.

Heads . . .

and tails. Ka-boom!

I can follow.

Can I lead?

A push.

I'm off.

A call.

I'm back.

And just in time for lunch.